JACOB'S HARD HEAD

By

Arleen Jamison

ISBN **9781532956867**

Dedication

To Jacob, who is the inspiration behind this book

Introduction

Jacob's Hard Head is a heartwarming story all about the antics of a precocious little boy. Anyone who has ever raised a child knows the delights and naughty moments of it all.

Sharing Jacob's trials through the eyes of his Grandma Arleen, gives us an insight into what being a parent/grandparent is truly about.

Throughout, Jacob's Hard Head is a comedic stream to make you smile, chuckle, and reflect on the hard heads you may have raised in your life and how they brought that joy to your heart.

Contents

Flowers Have No Rights.................9

 Patience Is a Virtue.....................14

Tempting Poppy's Tastebuds.............28

Laughter Is Good Medicine..............30

Education Is Key.........................41

Stone Age Vs. Cyberspace................48

Poppy's Fitness Advisor..................51

Jacob: Dude with An Attitude...........55

Casting Stones............................61

Talking Loud and Off-the-Wall.........64

Too Much Information...................67

 Not Enough Information.................70

Irresistible Force Vs Immovable Object73

Agreeing to Disagree.....................79

Follow Doctor's Orders...................82

Jacob's Lab Formula.....................84

Nighttime Tip............................89

Get It Delivered...........................91

Stating the Obvious........................94

Getting Two Cents Worth.................96

Older and Wiser............................98

Holiday Idea...............................99

Musical Observation.....................102

Get It Done...............................105

Acknowledgments

I would like to give thanks, first and foremost, to The Creator, for without HIM I can do nothing. I also would like to thank Skip Jamison, for your love, support, and encouragement to get this book done.

A massive thank you to Tina Jackson who has been behind me every step of the way; gently pushing and nudging me to get down to business and get it done. You are so much more than a long-time friend; you are, in my heart and mind my little sister. I so appreciate your love and support, thank you.

Flowers Have No Rights

Children are our most precious treasures.

Their wide-eyed innocence and, often, brutal

honesty are what endears them to us. They

drive us crazy and make us laugh. Such is the

case with a boy named Jacob who lived in the

second house from the corner and is an active

and noisy bundle of energy. He is all of five

and, like most kids at that stage, he's smart

and advanced for his age. He a cute little tyke

with sharp, light blue eyes that had just a hint

of devilment, sandy colored hair, and a smile

as bright as the sun. Born with the gift of gab,

he gives the term "motor mouth" a brand-new

meaning. He would do well as a prosecutor.

At times, he can be a most agreeable little

boy, and at other times he can be quite

contrary and hardheaded. One such occasion

was the time he was in Tia's yard riding his

ATV. Tia is a next-door neighbor, and Jacob

loved to play in her yard because it was

spacious and had a lot of flowers. So while he

was in her yard on this day, he was doing

figure 8s and circles when suddenly, he aims

the ATV straight at Tia's bed of Hostas and

plowed right through them. Tia was not

amused by that

but she still let him back some days later to

play, and while

riding his ATV, he roared through the flower

bed again! Luckily they survived, but

Mommy made him apologize and gave him a

stern warning and a timeout. Tia told him

that he was not allowed to ride in her yard

anymore. She had about had enough with his

reckless driving she said.

Patience Is A Virtue

Children are much known for their

impatience and Jacob was no exception. He

always wanted to have his way when he

wanted it. It was torture for him to have to put

his want on hold. He had the funniest ways of

showing it too, and sometimes not so funny

ways. One day, Jacob and I went into the

kitchen to make Jell-O. Jacob loves Jell-O, so

we decided to make the cherry flavor. I put

water on to boil, and when it was ready, I let

Jacob empty the envelope of Jell-O to the

water while I stirred it. Jacob added the

additional cup of cold water, and I got the

dessert plastic cups down to pour the gelatin.

Once all the cups were full, the gelatin that

was left over was poured into a glass bowl.

Everything was covered with plastic and

placed in the refrigerator to set.

I explained to Jacob that because the

gelatin was made late in the day, it wouldn't

be ready until the following day. He didn't

understand the concept of waiting at all, all he

Later the same day, Poppy and I were in our

bedroom watching TV when Jacob entered the

bedroom and asked if he could have some Jell-

O. Poppy and I both told him, again, it would

be ready the next day. Jacob left the bedroom

without a word, and the house grew quiet.

Now when kids get quiet, that is a sure sign

that trouble is afoot. He was quiet for so long

that I got concerned and decided to get up and

go check on him. I just had the feeling that he

was up to some mischief.

I got to the kitchen to find Jacob in the

middle of a red river of cherry Jell-O. He had

spilled the Jell-O in the glass bowl trying to

take it out of the fridge to

see if it was ready to eat. Jell-o on his clothes,

Jell-O on the shelf in the refrigerator, Jell-o

dripped down the front of it. Poppy walked

into the kitchen and went ballistic. Jacob was

always terrified of Poppy's anger and this

time he had really earned it.   Mommy and I

got paper towels and started cleaning. Jacob's

face crumbled and

tears flowed down his cheeks.

Little Jake was told one last time that the Jell-O

would be ready the following day.

Dennis the Menace has some stiff competition

but then there are times he can be dutiful and

sweet, and during those moments you

couldn't help but have your heart swell in

appreciation.

****

He demonstrated this act of immense

sweetness one day when I had back pain.

Jacob wanted to play ball in the backyard.

Knowing I couldn't do a lot of standing to toss

the ball, he ran and got a chair. "Here

grandma, I got you a chair since you're in

pain. Instead of standing and throwing the

ball you can sit and just kick it". "I'll run after

it and get it." I could've melted at that. He

wobbled over to place the chair correctly in

the perfect spot, so I could sit and participate

in the game with him undisturbed, or

unburdened. It was the sweetest thing ever.

After my open heart surgery, Jacob decided

to be my 24-hour nurse. He helped me with

my medications by getting the bottles I needed

and giving them to me. He was so dedicated

to his role, it was as though he was convinced

he had a part to play in getting me all healed. I

admit having him there, being all fussy about

me was very relaxing for me.

 One day he dressed up in his O.R. scrubs

from the past Halloween. He took my blood

pressure with his toy cuff and listened to my

heart with his stethoscope. When he was

done, he gave me his final findings, "Grandma

you can go back to work when you finish all

your pain pills." When I next saw my

cardiologist, I informed him that he had been

replaced! My cardiologist had laughed at that,

but little Jacob was very dedicated in his

desire to be my personal physician.

Tempting Poppy's Tastebuds

Once, when Jake was about five years old, we

decided were going to cook a meal together.

We had watched one of the cooking shows

and they were doing a dish called Osso Bucco.

I had to run out to get some of the ingredients

and Jake went with me. We arrived back

home and as we were going up the front steps,

we were talking about how we were going to

cook the dish. Jake in his excitement says.

"Grandma, it's going to be so good, Poppy's

gonna smack his wips!

I must say, after the little chef made it, it was

indeed incredibly good and Poppy really did

smack his wips, er, lips.

Laughter is Good Medicine

Jacob not only has sweet and naughty

moments, but he has some hilarious ones too.

His mother bought him pull-ups to wear to

bed at night, but during the day, he would

wear big boy underwear. When he was three

and a half, maybe just four years old, he woke

up before dawn one morning. His Poppy and I

were getting ready for work.

Poppy was in the bathroom, and I had to use

the toilet as well. Jacob walked into our

bedroom and hopped up on the bed. I said to

him, "You know Jake there's a problem.

Poppy is in the bathroom, and I must use it,

and we only have one. Jacob paused

and said, "Yeah we only have one." He

seemed as though he were deep in thought

and then

suddenly he brightened and said, "Grandma

would you like to borrow one of my pull-

ups?"

I had to stifle a laugh at the mental image that

suggested for me. How he could picture that I

could wear his pull-ups and take care of my

business in the absence of a toilet was

hilariously sweet.

Now, why didn't I think of that? In his little

mind that was the perfect solution. I could go

in the pull-up and then throw it away.

****

He was a ball of unusual encounters, and we

were almost always laughing because of

something he did. Later, I split my sides from

laughter when auntie told me about the

discussion she and Jacob had had. Jacob was

next door at the "diner" as he refers to auntie's

house, and they were discussing the

upcoming surprise party for Jacob's cousin.

She mentioned balloons and Jacob informed

her he could inflate balloons.

 Jacob went on to say that what was needed to

inflate balloons was "oxygen." The rest of the

world makes use of helium, but according to

Professor Jacob, it's oxygen.   Auntie then

asked him where he would get the oxygen.

Jacob said, "At the hospital."   Auntie asked

him how he would get it home. Jacob's reply

was, "Oh, grandma can carry it on her back!"

What a novel idea! Just strap a tank on my

back, and I could walk the 2.2 miles home

from the hospital. Why waste gas when

grandma has a good strong back? He was so

resourceful in his thinking, and his depth of

imagination never failed to leave us all

astounded. I didn't even bother to dispute or

argue with him, I just let him go with the flow.

Afterall, it was common knowledge that out of

the mouths of babes comes funny pearls of

wisdom.

****

Jake had a couple of styrofoam noodles in varying

lengths. We were in the dining room one day, and

he wanted to have a "noodle" fight. Before the

noodle match got started, he said to me, "We're

going to go outside in the yard, so nothing gets

broken, and Poppy won't have to burn up and yell.

I really don't want to hear him."

I was so taken aback and at the same time, so very

impressed that he had that much wisdom. For one,

he could predict his Poppy's reaction, and he also

has the good sense to want to avoid that.

I smiled at him, ruffling his hair gently and said,

"Right you are, let's take this noodle fight outside."

Education is Key

I find myself learning the darnedest things

when hanging around Jake. While in the

kitchen cooking Poppy's dinner, I overheard

Jake talking to his mother. He asked her if he

could turn on her air conditioner. She told

him she wasn't turning it on because it was

not an overly hot day. Now telling Jacob no

when he wants something is the equivalent of

waving a red flag at a bull. He asked his

mother again and again if he could turn the

AC on. Finally, she snapped 'no' at him one

last time. Jacob's response was, "But it's

raining!"

So, I guess, the lesson here is regardless of

the temperature and lack of humidity, if it's

raining that's the perfect reason to turn on

your AC.

****

When he was about three years old, Poppy

and I took Jacob on a trip to Kingston, NY.

Poppy wanted to visit a tool store there and to

try out a place to eat called the Texas

Roadhouse.

Both places are in the same vicinity, but one

has to do a little twisting and turning to

get from one to the other. Poppy left the tool

store, made a turn here, made a turn there,

then said to me, "I forgot where the place is."

We were at an intersection waiting for the

green light when the three-year-old personal

GPS in the rear child seat pipes up, "You keep

going stwait, keep going stwait, keep going

stwrait, and then make a wight!" Well, when

the light changed we went straight for a bit

and then there was a bend in the road to the

right. I glanced out the window and there on

the right was the place we were looking for—

Texas Roadhouse. Poppy and I were praising

him for being so smart and finding the

restaurant---one he had never been to before

that day I might add. He very matter of factly

informed us, "Yeah, see I know the woads!"

Indeed he knew the "woads," and it was just

our good sense that we had listened to him

and taken his directive.

Besides he did know the road's much better

than any GPS device, we could've bought.

He's cute and cheaper too.

Stone Age Vs. Cyberspace

Poppy is the inspiration behind the term

"technologically challenged." He can turn the

computer on, and that is the extent of his

computer knowledge…literally. What

possessed him to try to get on the internet this

particular day is beyond me. He usually

really never bothered with the stuff of that

nature. So as this is going on, I'm in the

kitchen cleaning, and he's on the computer

getting more frustrated by the minute. Little

Jacob who was only a little above 4 years of

age at this point was doing his best to help

poppy, but every time he would try to tell

Poppy how to get online, Poppy would yell at

him to be quiet and let him think. Poor Jacob,

at one point, said, "Poppy I twying to help

you!" Finally, I couldn't take it anymore, and

I called down the hallway to Poppy, "Stop

yelling at the boy and do what he says!" I

could hear Jacob telling him to click on this,

then click on that and, like magic, Poppy was

online.

To think, Poppy has the nerve to call Jacob

thick.

Poppy's Fitness Advisor

We loved to take Jacob to many different

places where he could learn and have a great

time. One beautiful day, we decided to take

him to a military museum. As he had grown,

he had developed a fascination for toy soldiers

and the armed forces, so this was to whet his

appetite for it. On this particular day, after

spending a couple of hours at the military

museum just off a military base, Jake, Poppy,

and I retired home where Jake immediately

got on the computer while Poppy and I

stretched out on the bed to relax. A few

minutes later Jake came bounding in the

bedroom. Now, his poppy is fond of

Wintergreen flavored mints and so is Jake. He

asked Poppy if he could have a mint. Poppy

told him he left them in the car and he'd get

them later. Jake's response was, "Could you

get them now? The exercise will do you

good!"

I had to agree with Jake on this one, Poppy did

need the exercise. With a grunt Poppy got up

to go to the car for the flavored mint. It really

was amazing how a little boy of four could

press his demands and be heard. It was even

more amazing the depth of his knowledge.

Jacob: The Dude with an Attitude

Children and their attitude sometimes, it

can leave us bewildered, and Jacob often left

us bewildered. One beautiful, sunny

afternoon, Jake and I were cruising down the

road on our way to pick Poppy up from work.

I was behind the wheels and Jacob was seated

in the back of the car with his sippy cup filled

with milk. As we're driving along, Jacob

finished his milk and wanted me to take the

empty cup from him. When he demanded I

take the cup, I paused for a second to oblige

but then we were driving, and I figured well it

could wait till we hit a red light. This was

mainly because I didn't feel comfortable doing

that at 40 mph. I tried telling Jacob I would

take the cup when we stopped at a red light.

Trying to reason with a three-year-old is like

ordering a rock to stand up and dance. He

kept insisting I take that darn cup until finally,

I snapped and said to him I was not going to

collect that cup until we came to a stop.

Jacob's face turned as dark and fierce as a

raging storm as he said to me, "Grandma,

you're really adabating me."

I looked in the rearview mirror and said,

"You want me to reach back and take a cup

away. We're going 40 mph and could run the

risk of getting into an accident where both of

us end up with bad boo-boos in the "mercy"

room (he couldn't say emergency), and I'm

aggravating *you*???

Even at three, I think he could see how silly he

was being.   He dissolved into peals of giggles.

I found myself wondering how did he know

the word "aggravate," he really was

precocious for his age. Jacob has the most

gorgeous, light blue eyes and when he smiles

they light up like glittering blue diamonds.

When we approached the red light, as

promised, I took the sippy cup.

Casting Stones

Jacob and his poppy are very much alike.

Both are male, and that alone makes putting

up with them a challenge. Neither has

patience, and both are thick headed. No

doubt that's why they always butt heads.

Last week the three of us went grocery

shopping. When we got home, we began

unloading the car. Jake had a bag, I had a bag

and Poppy had a couple of bags. Poppy has

an old cart that he repurposed. A nut here, a

bolt there, four blown up wheels and that's

what he uses to haul groceries around the

back of the house. Jacob asked him, "Poppy,

you want me to get the grocery cart?" Poppy

told him, "No Jacob, we don't need it."

Somewhat disappointed and a little annoyed,

Jacob replied, "Aw Poppy, why do you have

to do everything the hard way?" My jaw

dropped, and I couldn't speak. Jacob,

accusing someone of doing something the

hard way? There has never been a more

glaring case of the pot speaking ill of the

kettle!

Talking Loud and Off the Wall

Trying to have a conversation with Jake can be

interesting if not a bit confusing. I suppose

that is the way it is with children of his age.

One day, I called the house from work. I let

the phone ring three, maybe four times before

I had to hang up because the phone at work

was ringing so I needed to answer to it. A few

days later, Jake was in our bedroom with me

and decided I needed to be instructed as to the

proper way to make a phone call. He gives me

this stern look like a professor about to school

his students and begins "Grandma when you

call you have to wait and let the phone ring.

Poppy can't move so fast and needs time to

answer it." Poppy chuckled at his explanation,

and with a sigh, I explained to him that

sometimes when I call I have to hang up

because the work phone rings and it's my job

to answer it. He said, "Well it doesn't matter.

Someone from Texas could call this number,

and you'd still have to let the phone ring."

No sense, no rhyme or reason but it was Jake's

claim on having the last word

Too Much Information

Kids say the darndest things at the darndest

times. Two-year-old Jake and his uncle were

playing some silly game that involved a lot of

high pitched squealing and giggling on Jake's

part. He loved this play time with his uncle

because

well his uncle had all the energy to swing him

up and down which Jacob really loved. As he

toddled down the hallway, his uncle grabbed

him from behind and swung him up to sit him

on his shoulders. Just as his uncle was about

to seat him, Jacob, for unknown reasons

announces, "I HAVE DIARRHEA!" at the top

of his lungs.

One second he was hovering above his

uncle's shoulders. The next, he was hastily

but safely placed back on the ground. We will

never know what possessed him to say that.

His mother checked. He did not have

diarrhea. He, however, found that little

incident hilarious, especially the horrified look

on his uncle's face.

Not Enough Information

One day, while in the kitchen, Jake came

down the hallway and went into his mother's

room to ask if he could have a Strawberry

Shortcake. On one of her shopping trips, she

bought the shortcake shells. She told Jake he

could have one of the shells only. He then

comes in the kitchen and says, "Mommy said I

could have Strawberry Shortcake." I, not

knowing his mother said only the shell, fixed

him a Strawberry Shortcake complete with the

cake, strawberries, and whipped cream. Jake

takes the confection in his mother's room to

show her. I hear her say to him, "I didn't say

you could have all of that. I said the cake

only." Jake's response was, "See, I told you

Grandma was going to spoil me!" I had a

feeling he had known precisely what he was

doing and had deliberately orchestrated it like

that. For one thing, he was brilliant I have to

give him that. It was also a very informative

incident. It was even funnier how I could learn

so much real-life lessons which were valuable

from a young kid.

Irresistible Force Vs. Immovable Object

There is nothing in the world like watching an

older generation trying to teach a younger

know-it-all how something should be done.

Makes for comical entertainment because no

one wants to relent to the other and each one

felt they were more informed than the other.

Jacob had his toy train track set up on the

living room floor. He's creative for his age

because at this point he is just 5 years of age

and is quite the little perfectionist. He was

adjusting this and rearranging that to get the

track just right. His grandfather, sitting in the

chair, was attempting to show him how to

connect the track so the train would run

smoothly.

Poppy: Jake, you need to put the straight

track on the other end.

Jake: I know, I know. I don't want to put it

there.

Poppy: Go get another straight piece and put

it at that other end.

Jake: What end?

Poppy: That end right there.

Jake: Where?

Poppy: Right there.

Jacob places the track where he *thought* Poppy

was talking about.

Poppy: No, no, no! Not there.

Jake: Where then? You just told me to put it

here.

Finally, after much intense discussion back

and forth, the track was assembled, and the

train was able to make all its stops.

Agree to Disagree

Jacob and Poppy were having one of their

head-butting difference of opinions. Jake

would say something and Poppy would come

back with something totally opposite. Finally,

I heard Jacob say, "I'm just going to leave this

and do something else." He came down the

hallway to the kitchen where I was and said,

"Poppy has to argue with everything I say.

There's no talking to him!" He went back

down the hallway shaking his head and

shrugging his shoulders as if trying to figure

out how he could have a Poppy who argues

with everything *he* says. It's a good thing

they're not married I thought to myself, even

as I wondered how Jake could sound so

mature at his age.

Follow Doctor's Orders

I was folding laundry in the bedroom one day after a recent rotator cuff repair. Part of the discharge instructions was to keep the shoulder iced multiple times a day. I had an ice machine that handled the job beautifully.

It was nearly lunchtime, and I mentioned to Jacob that I hadn't done cold therapy on my shoulder as of yet. Five-year-old Jake didn't

miss a beat and wisely said, "Well, you have

to Grandma. It's the only thing that's going to

help you." "Please do the ice machine now."

He was my little doctor during that time.

Priceless.

Jacob's Lab Formula

Playing doctor was really a fun thing for

Jacob, but he took it with all seriousness. At

this point, we all believed his future career

would be along the medical field. This is

because of the way he rushes to assist any of

us when we are down. So I'm lying in bed one

night my shoulder was really throbbing. I had

taken a painkiller a few minutes before and

was waiting for the medication to take effect.

Jacob was on the bed with Poppy and I. I

turned to him and said, "Doctor, my shoulder

hurts." He immediately went into doctor

mode, jumped down from the bed and dashed

into his room. When he returned, I had to

hide my laughter. Jacob had a scrub hat

pulled way down over his forehead. Dressed

only in a pull-up, he was carrying his little

doctor bag with a play stethoscope around his

neck. He hopped back on the bed and told me

he had to listen to my heart. After a minute he

said my heart was going, "thumpity-thump,

thumpity-thump." I can't say how glad I was

to hear that it was thumping. He then pulled

out a play syringe explaining that he was

going to give me 4ccs of the "formula" mixed

with the flu vaccine. I asked what the formula

was even as I gave a mock grimace as though I

was scared of the needle. He said it was a

unique recipe. When combined with the flu

vaccine

it's better and faster. It works in two minutes.

As he was saying this, I actually did start

feeling some relief. Of course, I have no doubt

it was the pain pill taking effect, but I gave

credit to the thorough exam and care I

received from my little fhedoctor. He

patiently explained, "When you combine the

recipe and flu vaccine it relieves pain. I

wonder if doctors today are aware of this?

A Nighttime Tip

It was the end of a busy day. Poppy, Jacob and I were stretched out on the bed watching TV. Poppy yawned and said, "See, it's 7:29 pm and I can barely keep my eyes open."

Jacob, with an ever-ready answer for everything, replied, "So take some Nyquil and go to sleep!" I looked over at Poppy and

Poppy looks at me. We seem to be thinking

the same thing, so he knows what Nyquil is?

In any case, after dealing with the two of them

all day long, I was so in agreement with the

last portion of that advice. They both needed

to follow it.

his eyes lit up like two sparkling blue

diamonds. Sometime later in the day he asked

me when it would arrive. I told him the

company said it should come on Monday. It

might come Monday but it might not. To that,

Jacob said, "Well, if it doesn't come, get them

on the phone, so I can yell at them." I wonder

if getting yelled at by a six-year-old would get

his car delivered faster?

Stating the Obvious

Sitting in the living room one day, Jacob was

on the floor playing, and I was preparing to do

my finger stick. I got the glucometer all set

with the strip and put the lancet in place. I

positioned the pen and pressed the button to

release the lancet. I muttered out loud, "Ow!

That didn't feel right." Jacob, with an answer

for everything, as usual, glanced at me and

asked, "Was it supposed to?"

I think he was the inspiration behind the term,

'smart aleck.' He was indeed smart, and his

smartness was very refreshing for us. The

house seemed to come alive with brightness

and pleasant feelings when Jake was around.

Getting Two Cents Worth

After cleaning out my closet, Poppy was

hanging some new shirts I bought for me. He

said to me, "We need more hangers." I told

him, "I don't have anymore." He said he'd

have to look in his closet for some. Now Jake

was sprawled in the recliner playing with one

of his toys. As Poppy walked by on the way

to his closet, Jacob pipes up, "Yeah, why don't

you do that honey?"

Poppy and I looked at him and then at each

other and smiled. I have no clue where he

gets some of the stuff he says.

Older and Wiser

Jacob is now a big boy of eight. He and his

mother were living with Poppy and me when

this book was first started. They have since

moved out to a home of their own. Jacob still

comes to visit and spend sleepovers with us.

Just as when he was younger, he continues to

amuse us with the things he says.

Holiday Idea

Eight-year-old Jacob and his poppy were

having a phone conversation a few days

before Christmas. Jake called to ask if he

could have a sleepover on December 24th.

Poppy thought for a moment and said, "Jacob,

that's Christmas Eve." This was Christmas

2016.

I want to be with you and grandma, then you

can take me home at 6 o'clock in the morning

so I can have Christmas with mom and dad."

Poppy told him if it was ok with his mom, he

was more than welcome to stay. He told Jake

he would pencil him in for the 24th.

The call ended with, "You have a good

evening, and I love you."

"Good night, Poppy."

However, this sleepover never took place.

Jacob, the genius, realized since he has moved,

Santa would be delivering his presents to his

house as opposed to ours.

Musical Observation

This past Thanksgiving, Poppy and I were

invited out for dinner. Not wanting to walk in

empty-handed, it was decided we would

bring holiday cookies. We split the cooking

making up into assigned jobs. Poppy did the

baking, while Jake and I did the decorating.

Usually, when music is played in the house or

the car, it's Poppy's country western favorites.

I love listening to music when I work so this

time I got my external speaker and chose a

pop music playlist on my phone. As Jake and

I began our cookie decorating, Jake listened

for a moment, and then he said, "Oh cool,

something besides cowboy music…In this

house!"

Get It Done

Recently, I had to go to the eye doctor. Poppy

had to take me as I was getting my eyes

dilated. Jacob was with us. We went, I had

my eye exam, and then we left to go home.

We got to the exit and were waiting for a

break in traffic so Poppy could make a left

turn. Poppy kept asking me if it was from the

right. I told him repeatedly that it clear was.

Nine-year-old Jacob, sounding impatient and

disgusted, pipes up from the back seat, "Just

hit the gas pedal already!"

Could Poppy possibly need a refresher

driving course with Jake as his instructor?

This book began when my four year old

grandson was cutting paper into booklets and

stapling them together. He announced,

"Grandma, we're going to have a book sale in

the driveway. You be the author and the

illustrator, I'll be the man that makes the

money". Even at four, he had given the book

sale a lot of thought. Get Grandma to do all

the work and he sits back and reaps the

benefits. As I thought about it though, the

idea appealed more and more. I decided it

would be really special to write a book about

the little boy who was the inspiration behind

it.   That is how Jacob's Hard Head was born.

Thanks for reading Jacob's Hard Head. I hope

you enjoyed it as much as I did writing it.